Aussie Bush Yarns

Happy Reading,

Neil Hulm.

AUTHOR	Neil Hulm
ILLUSTRATIONS	Keith Nickels Greg Bradley Craig Coleman
PRINTING AND TYPESETTING	Wilkie Watson publications Pty Ltd, Tumut
COVER	Refer to page 38

Hulm, Neil, 1930—
Aussie Bush Yarns.

Includes Index.
ISBN 0 9590032 1 5

Nickels, Keith.   1960
Bradley, Greg   1956
Coleman, Craig   1965

FOREWORD

These stories concern happenings from the bushlands of various parts of Australia and although most of the yarns are quite true, there are a number that the reader is not expected to believe. The main idea of putting "Aussie Bush Yarns" together is that, hopefully, the readers get a little enjoyment from this very small part of our Australian history.

Neil Hulm,
Lavington,
N.S.W. 2641
1986

CONTENTS

CONTENTS

Inspector C. Bell

As you cast your lines and set your nets
Where the high winds break and roar;
Did you turn your eyes with a furtive glance
To the scrub by the edge of the shore?

Now this is a tale most fishermen know,
So many had learned it well;
By mountain lakes and cold clear streams,
Lies the legend of Charlie Bell.

For Charlie Bell was known to all;
To those users of illegal gear,
In the waters of our National Park,
Where he planted a doubting fear.

He'd felt twin barrels scan his ribs,
Odd times been thrown in the drink;
Did this worry Inspector Bell?
No — Not a sign of shiver or blink.

As Chas strolled up to a fisherman's camp
He'd be wearing a down-town smile,
But the brain behind that leathery face
Would outwit a fox's guile.

By the Geehi, camped were Tom and Fred,
Their fire burning high and bright.
Tom quoted, "Fred, settle down old mate,
We're free of old Charley tonight."

"I met Chas and his wife at Cooma town
With a caravan, heading to the sea,
We've plenty of nets, a little Red Crown,
A night of nights this will be!"

As daylight broke the boys awoke,
Then pulled their catch to the bank,
But the little bloke Fred turned a shade red,
As his heart and his hopes both sank.

With a "Pssst! Hey Tom, I reckon we're gone,
And I don't think I feel so well,
For along the shore I reckon I saw
The face of old Charley Bell."

"Naw, that's not Charlie, just too much Rum,
He's gone to Tathra - to the coast."
"Well if that's not Charlie," muttered young Fred,
"It must be his flamin' ghost!"

Chas, of course had doubled back
And he won their nets and lines,
Of course he didn't leave them bare,
For they both won hefty fines.

By the water's edge at Eucumbene
Were camped two fishermen keen,
With a bell attached to a set line,
Quite sure they couldn't be seen.

As darkness came the winds died down,
Then the bell rattled strong and clear;
Those fishermen strode to the water's edge,
To the trout they sought so dear.

The leader spoke, "That's one we've caught,
Just a couple more will be swell."
Then a soft voice spoke, "I've caught two".
'Twas Charlie that rattled the bell!!

The years roll on, we thank you Charles,
For a job, and a job done well;
The fishing still remains so grand.
Well done, Charley Bell.

The Days Of Old Bay

That good old bay is fat and slow,
His joints are stiff and he must have rest,
He still snorts loud, but it's only show,
For age grows fast, especially on the best.

His thoughts may race a little off hand,
To when his feet were bare and sore,
Or that snowfall on the flat land
Where he hadn't seen a fall before.

Or of the time he lost his rider,
The reins hooked on a dry limb, tight,
Did he wonder, if the old dog was wiser
As it stayed with him through the night?

There are times he'll slightly shiver
As he looks out towards the hills,
At the memories of brumbies, he'll quiver,
Of the chase, and the many thrills.

The young colts rear and paw the air,
Then race, in the morning sun,
'I could beat them all, if I was to care,
But I better not spoil their fun.'

The gate to the stockyard open,
He'd walk in, then wheel and snort,
Perhaps just pretending and hopin'
For a steer or a colt to be caught.

Scarcely a trot can the old horse raise
And the days of his toils are spent,
That's where he'll stay, for the rest of his days,
Where he'll dream, to his heart's content.

The Big Wet — '71

The floods were down on the Hunter,
Slightly mixed with a touch of mud;
Travellers cursed that roads were cut,
While the whole town cursed the flood.

But the Pub was dry at Aberdeen,
When in blew the Sergeant, stout,
"Water surrounds old Brownie's home,
We must get his furniture out."

"Six volunteers, raise your hands,
This job we must not flunk,
So leave your ale behind you, boys,
You're no good to me if you're drunk!!"

The Thames plugged on through driving rain,
Right up to old Brownie's shack,
While water spread from Dartmouth Creek,
'Midst thunder and lightning cracks.

Water had lapped the bottom step
That led to a damp back floor,
Those eager lads worked like slaves,
Urged along by the Sergeant's roar.

The task near done, the water rose,
Clear over the steps, raced free,
Doug backed out through the doorway,
He was lumping the prized T.V.

If a man goes back, 'tis said, 'bad luck',
And a luck that we never seek,
Doug missed the step, and damn near drowned,
The T.V. bobbed away in the creek!!

Learn A Little

It was many long, long years ago,
That I first had a look at a local show,
I was young and shy, in a nervous state,
As I paid my sixpence at the gate.

Slowly and quietly I looked around,
Quite fascinated, with things I found;
Then I moved along as I heard a shout,
"There's an extra pound if you knock him out!"

It was Sharman's troupe with their big marquee,
And a spruiker yelled, "It's the best you'll see."
Then a challenge called; and a challenger found,
To fight the champ for a couple of pounds.

As I didn't have the entrance fee,
The back of the tent was the way for me.
I watched those boxers fight hard and neat,
But the travelling men were hard to beat.

There were sideshows, dolls and knock'em downs,
And lots of folk from neighbouring towns;
Some travelled by horse and others in cars;
The brass band screeched like a flock of galahs.

A wild steer ride too, was the usual thing,
I decided then I would give it a fling;
Compared with those cowboys, my age was half,
But I'd practised at home on a poddy calf.

So they tightened the rope and opened the gate
And that beast exploded with a hell of a rate;
Then our heads somehow clashed, he threw me
    high,
But I'd won five shillings and a beaut black eye!!

There were cattle, sheep and fowls penned up;
Terriers, cattle dogs and Kelpie pups,
In the pavillion were cakes, fruit and jam,
Linen and knitting and a big smoked ham.

The horses in the ring were shiny and flash,
But some hit the hurdles with an awful bash;
The high jump was the most wonderful sight,
For the horses rose as if in flight.

A fat lady wobbled as she trotted her dog,
Stumbled a little when they jumped a log;
She returned to the judge, quite sure of a prize,
Then reefed the dog's tail towards the skies.

The ambulance man had tickets to sell,
"You pick 'em, we pay 'em," his continuous yell.
A pieman roared 'til his voice grew hoarse;
His apron smothered in tomato sauce.

A great day's fun was had by all,
Most went home sober, a few stepping tall;
I hopped on my horse and cantered away
And felt that I'd learned a little that day.

Red Roan Rogue

The start of this tale
Was at a cattle sale,
Where a Bull caught the eye of a lad;
The colour red roan,
Two years old, well grown,
He didn't look at all too bad.

The lad thought, 'swell',
As the hammer fell,
Drove the Bull ten miles home;
That Bull was quiet,
Did everything right,
But a holy terror to roam.

At the break of dawn
He would be gone,
We'd search, while ever there was light,
Then bring him back
Through rough bush tracks
And lock him in the yard for the night.

MERRY XMAS

14

The oldies had gone
To the town in the morn',
To the local, for a yarn and a 'few'.
When riding back,
Met on the track,
That Bull, he was travelling too.

So they turned on the pace
As that rogue Bull raced,
Along a fence down hill, they flew;
With a swerve that flyer
Jumped over the wire,
And the stock horse stuck like glue.

A workman on the place
And us young'uns saw the race,
We were poking about, close to home,
He said, "They're mad, a disgrace
For grown men to chase."
As we laughed to see the old man thrown.

The year about to fold,
That Bull to be sold,
He was costing us far too many rides,
When he came a racing back
Then rejoined his own pack,
With a big MERRY XMAS on his sides.

In bright paint of white,
The bull full of fright,
For he'd raced to his own paddock, flat,
There was someone who knew,
They had the right clue,
For that rogue stayed at home after that.

The Road to Jindabyne

Oh, to dally through the mountains
From the open Western Plains,
Where Snow Grass, Gums and Heather
Form a carpet on the Range.

The grey snow clouds still gather
As they did since start of time;
And the Snowy races wildly
By the road to Jindabyne.

Rainbow trout rise high and play
In the shining snowy lakes;
A screeching call of Black Cockatoos,
Before the snow clouds break.

Those lonely days were pushed behind
With the horse teams' fast decline;
Now folk drive up in thousands
On the Road to Jindabyne.

Wild flowers spread for a hundred miles,
Snow Gums wave in the breeze,
Wild dogs howl a mournful cry,
On the fall to the Southern Seas.

Through gorges thick with Mountain Ash
The road gangs worked overtime,
To cut their tracks and level out
The Road to Jindabyne.

There's a faded, broken wagon,
So grand in the days of old;
And from every ridge and gully
There's a story to be told.

Oh, they're racing down the mountain;
Up the Coastal roads, so fine;
So we'll pack up and travel too,
On the Road to Jindabyne.

The Blower 1942

'Twas a racehorse, The Blower;
There was no horse raced slower,
A useless big chestnut, white faced,
Bought and respected, tried and neglected;
Ran last at all times when he raced.

The lead pony outpaced him
When Grandfather raced him;
His legs like a blind man on stilts;
As a sheep in the snow, that horse couldn't go;
Like an old willow tree with the wilts.

He raced wide at the start,
It would fair break your heart
When he struggled way back at the rear;
With a high jiggling head and legs widely spread,
Like a camel with acute diarrhoea.

So The Blower was sacked,
With the bridle then cracked
On his tail as he cantered away;
Let go loose like a child, where bush horses ran
        wild
In the hills, he soon joined the fray.

Now with Grandad's stern voice
Us young lads had no choice,
"Keep good watch on that chestnut," he cried.
We found the horse later, was a dead as a 'tater';
Who would tell Grandad, The Blower had died.

The coin that was tossed
Was a dud, as I lost,
And the courage I had, lost its gore;
But Grandad then spoke, quite enjoying his joke,
"That horse hasn't ever done that before!!"

A Man, A Boy And Their Chooks

The sale was over, with all goods gone,
From cattle through to rusty hooks;
The crowd departed, but an item missed,
And that was a lot of thirty odd chooks.

A phone call made — must do the right thing —
Those fowls were caught, to be taken down,
In a battered old 'ute, with netting atop;
Give them to Granny, by the edge of town.

Fowls were all loaded, midst a hell of a din,
Rattles and squawks; all seemed to swell,
But the rough gravel road proved a little much;
From the back of the 'ute, the tail board fell.

A mile from home they glanced slowly back,
Those fowls raced wild, it seemed every way.
The young lad drawled in a low pitched voice,
"Whatever on earth will my Granny say?"

The old man squawked in his squeeky tone,
While giving the youngster 'get cracking' looks,
"Never mind what Granny might say,
Just get and catch those blinkin' chooks!!"

But the chooks were racing homeward bound,
With a big red rooster showing the way;
Those chooks weren't caught 'till the following
        morn'
On the fowl house roost at the break of day.

Hands Of The Bushmen

"Stay close that mare in the lead, Joe,
Turn the bay colt fast, if he wheels
We won't hold the pace, the mob will race
As if the Devil were at their heels."

That's where we find our best horsemen,
They race where the scrub is green,
Astride the back of a fiery hack
And their deeds are rarely seen.

Hands in the bush; forget it,
They'll be where they ought to be,
For if misplaced, you'll be disgraced,
Wrapped around the butt of a tree.

No reins, no horse; that's big trouble,
You'll be upside down in the bogs,
Or beneath your horse in a wombat hole,
Perhaps caught in a criss-cross of logs.

Don't get ideas you're a horseman
If you train a few horses to race,
You don't become a stud master
If you run a few mares on the place.

An odd bushy rides somewhat slackly
And relaxes if no flying manes,
He may appear to be off in a dream world,
But he knows how to handle those reins.

They've raced, caught and handled wild horses,
Scrub bulls, through the hills and the drains;
We take off our hats to those horsemen;
The bushies, the masters of reins.

Silent Winter On The Range

The mountain men have mustered,
Cattle and sheep are away;
Winter's snows have clustered,
But we must search for the strays.

When snow starts to fly, the black cocky's cry,
Move away to the foot of the hills;
The trout have gone, under creek banks to spawn;
The whole land is silent and still.

We miss the sheep, their ringing bleat,
The cattle have left the range;
No more can we hear the rattle of gear,
For the outfit is down on the plains.

We miss it all, the scrub bull's call,
A brumby's shrill whistle at night,
Or the work dog's growl at a dingo's howl
As they stood and were ready to fight.

The Bogong moths have moved away,
Gone to much lower ground;
The stunted snow gums stand alone,
For there's no wild life to be found.

The singing birds have vanished,
Bull ants are in rotting logs,
Wild ducks have flown to the flatlands,
We don't hear the crickets and frogs.

As you camped on the tops, as often as not,
You'd promise yourself that you'd go;
But to live a free life is a heaven's delight,
Just as sure as the cold of the snow.

Little Bindi

Two barefooted boys, with ferret and nets,
And an ill bred dog, just a family pet.
Chasing rabbits for the whole weekend,
Earning money; perhaps a little to spend.

The little dog barked, so far, far away,
Boys wondered what he was chasing today;
They peered about at the trees and rocks,
Then suddenly spotted a big red fox.

Brer fox jumped into a hollow log,
But didn't outfox Little Bindi, the dog.
For the little dog snarled and the fight began;
The lads with sticks, to the log then ran.

24

In the hollow log, 'twas as dark as night,
Towards the centre, they could hear the fight;
So they blocked an end, at the other stayed,
And waited for the fox and silently prayed.

The cunning old fox had developed a thirst,
He pushed Little Bindi from the log head first.
And the hand of the lads, not the hand of fate,
Brought the sticks down fast, hard and straight.

The fox gave a snarl and away he fled;
And the faithful dog? Well, he fell down dead.
Living now in the sky is the game little dog,
But I doubt if he chases a fox in a log.

Must Have Cream

The cows had turned dry
As the green grass died,
Sent to the paddock till they calved.
A few months break
Was quite easy to take,
As our work was almost halved.

When the cows were out,
There were two young louts,
From town, to the farm came to stay,
All they could scream,
Was, "We want cream."
They'd roar and whinge all day.

"We'll milk the cows,
We want some cream!"
For two long days they'd wail.
The boss gave a sly grin,
"Righto boys, get them in,
Go ahead, put the cows in the bail."

KNICKELS 86

Barefoot and red faced,
Those young louts chased
The milkers around the paddock for a while.
Through the gate ahead
Then into the shed,
And the young 'uns were both full of smiles.

Quiet-looking — and near,
Was a big black steer,
Had been running with the cows all spring.
They grabbed his tail
To put him in the bail,
And wound up with a kick in the shin.

The racket that flew
From the cowyard grew,
Was the way to milk cows, it seems.
For those lads thought,
The harder they fought,
The cows would give out more cream.

They left for the house
As quiet as a mouse,
Not a speck of cream had they made.
Bruises by the stack
Clothes torn off their back,
And plastered like a cowyard spade.

The Hand of Old Sod

We were caught in a laneway,
Miles from town, after wood;
We'd loaded the 'ute
To the top of the hood.

The track a bit greasy
And wheels in a spin,
We just couldn't make it
For the rubbers were thin.

Old Sod, a bush farmer
Lived a bit further down;
He used to ride horses
To get into town.

No matter who travelled
That track, fast or slow,
They'd pick up Old Sod;
His horse then let go.

They'd cart back his goods
Or what ever he bought,
Gave him a ride home
And always charged nought.

Then many years later
He cleaned out his shed,
Old Sod bought a motor;
His old horses were dead.

'Here comes Old Sod
On his shiny new bike,
He'll give us a push,
That will save us a hike.

Our dog being normal
Walked onto the track,
Peered up at Old Sod
And his fancy new hack.

But Old Sod raced by
Into town for a grog,
With a "Howdy gentlemen",
And "Git to blazes dog!!"

Publican Dick

They sing and they yell at Holbrook Hotel,
Dick laughs, "If I'm lucky they'll drown."
Lester sits quietly and Donnie sings brightly,
While The Crow insists on acting the clown.

Dust storms will ravage, race, twist and choke,
For many a month on the Plains; it's no joke,
With a huge friendly grin, the Publican cried,
"Don't worry none boys, she's sure wet inside."

"Come in, come in quick," said Publican Dick,
"'Tis paradise inside my mortar and brick;
Outside, dust chokes you, or mud cracks your
        hide,
But the temperature's perfect, just lovely inside!"

The heavens let loose, their big storage tanks,
Rivers were full and a-bursting their banks;
With a huge friendly grin, the Publican cried,
"Don't worry none boys, she's sure dry inside!"

Thirty dollars a hundred, from shearers he'd get,
Dick knew their value was fifty-odd 'wet';
"Eleven's the time folks, we've come to an end,
Middy sir? Thank you, cheers to you friend."

"Rum sire? By jove, that's a right smart goatee;
No, put it away sir, that last one's on me,
Might have one with you; clock's a little quick,
Don't think we've met sir, I'm Publican Dick!!"

KNICKELS 86

One On Me

One night I was staying with my uncle, who lived about one mile up the road from Tumbarumba. This was during my school days in 1942.

I was about to take off to school next morning when it was suggested that I leave my horse in the paddock for the day and ride a push bike, then collect my horse after school.

As I hadn't ridden a bike previously, I was a bit dubious about this. However, I decided to give it a go. After receiving instructions on how to stop this machine, as it didn't have any brakes, I hopped on and wobbled on my way.

I had only gone a few hundred yards and being downhill, the bike was gathering too much speed, so I did as instructed and put my foot on the front tyre near the fork to ease her down a bit. I then promptly hit the dirt with the bike on top of me. I hopped up cursing and wheeled it down the hill. At the bottom there was a small bridge with two posts on either side, but without guide rails. Without much thought, I pushed the bike close to a post to get a kick off when I hopped on. Aboard again, the bike gave a wobbly and fell in the creek, with me undernearth it again.

I scrambled out, dripping wet and walked the rest of the way to school. After school I went back to the creek, pulled the bike out and pushed it back to the shed where it belonged. It was many years later before I had another ride on a bike.

The Shanty at Clover Flat

We were fishing in the mountains
Where the Toolong*used to flow,
And to educate the youngsters
There was Sugar, Matt and Joe.

In the darkness rode up Cecil,
With his rowdy way of fun,
"Wild cattle on The Booby,
Do you hear them bawling, son?"

Next in came stockman Clarrie,
From Yaouk through the snow,
The man who rode The Rebel,
At the Tumba' Rodeo.

They talked of bucking horses,
Told stories wide and tall;
The young lads watched in wonder,
With their backs against the wall.

They sipped Red Crown in Toolong Hut;
With gum wood burning bright,
While this yarn unfolded slowly,
By the lantern's flickering light.

'Twas about a bottle of potent Rum,
And a hollow Mountain Ash tree,
A trusty old black sheep dog
And a man who got on the spree.

Young Clarrie Rees, the stockman,
Had stayed in Tumba' town,
Spent far too long in the local,
He had drunk enough to drown.

Homeward bound by Clover Flat,
Said, "My drinking will now cease."
Wrote clearly on a bottom of rum,
"Good drop," signed, Clarrie Rees.

He wrapped the bottle in a bag,
Placed the goods in a hollow tree,
Covered it up with candle bark,
Said, 'No more booze for me!'

Along came Matt and Sugar
Searching for dry fire wood;
They discovered the hidden liquor,
Both declared it was extra good.

A nip apiece, the cork replaced,
Just before they left the flat;
Then another message written,
"The goods are good," signed Matt.

'Twas Cecil and Norm at Clover Flat,
Next year in the cold and damp;
Their dog scratched in the hollow tree,
In search of a dry, warm camp.

The goods were rediscovered,
Norm had the barest taste,
But Cecil gulped the contents down,
Spoke, "Boy, one must not waste!!"

The fiery rum began to work,
Cec turned a glowing pink,
Roared, "Boy, rush down to the Creek,
Bring me a long cold drink!"

Cecil rode off down the track,
He didn't know right from wrong,
Down by the Devil's Elbow,
Wildly singing his song.

"Wild cattle on The Booby,
Big brindles, black and roans."
The saddle slipped from his old horse,
Cecil rolled amongst the stones!!

When cold south winds are blowing,
And your muscles frozen numb,
You'll find that life will brighten,
If you take a nip of rum.

The moral of this story,
Should you take a little swig;
Put the cork back in the bottle;
Don't be such a greedy pig!!

*Toolong: This area is now under the waters of the
Tooma Dam, Snowy Mountains Scheme.

Gypsy The Punter

According to Doug, Gypsy was a good punter with a bad memory, but could remain poker faced for many hours, and really expected all concerned to believe his statements.

After the races had finished, Doug met Gypsy at the local hotel.

Doug asked Gypsy how he had fared with the bookies. Gypsy said, "Won a 'hunned', Doug." Doug replied, "Well done, old mate," then moved off to have a few beers with the chaps he had entered the bar with.

A couple of hours later Doug was moving around a little in the bar and heard Gypsy telling a chap, "I won a couple of 'hunned' today, mate."

About ten o'clock Gypsy was getting a little the worse for wear and started moving about, having a chat to different people. He had a cigarette in one hand and a ten ounce glass of beer in the other and was at this stage, spilling more than he was drinking. He was getting close to Doug, so Doug thought that he would get in first, "You had a good day, eh mate?"

Gypsy slurred, "Won five 'hunned' Dougie, five 'hunned'. Hey Dougie, could you lend me fifty 'til next week?"

Those Brainless Sheep?

Years ago as our world turned peaceful,
Many stations were given the chop,
Plans were laid, land surveyed
For Soldier Settlement Blocks.

Money loaned at a reasonable rate,
Helped the new settlers along,
They worked away and made things pay,
The number quite small, that went wrong.

They mostly came from farmlands,
A few were reared by the sea,
An odd recruit, worked in his suit,
Didn't know a cow from a tree.

Shearers on the board and ready,
Sheep in the back of the yard,
The shed door tied back open
And rain was coming down hard.

The raw one said, "I've heard before
That sheep don't have a brain,
I left that door wide open,
They still stayed out in the rain!!"

He'd seen horses in carts and sulkies,
Travelling easy and slow,
So he caught a horse, harnessed it up,
Then expected it to go.

It went all right, kicked with fright,
Raced like a trained greyhound,
Tore a clothes line apart, smashed the cart;
The new chum thrown to the ground.

He once swung his axe, ringbarked a patch
Of timber down by the yard,
Said, "The green trees are quite easy,
But those dry ones terrible hard."

The wool cheque in his pocket
And dressed like the son of a Lord,
Took off on a coastal holiday,
In a sparkling brand new Ford.

A month in clover soon passed over,
As explained when a message came,
"In debt deep, shear the sheep;
Home on the old goods train!"

As The Timeless Burning Sands

Where the dry creek beds are winding
Their way through the scrub bound plain,
A young boundary rider was working,
'Twas years since he'd seen a fair rain.

For the North West boundary riders
Have the worries that come to few,
Where the kangaroos will push out holes
And let the wild dogs through.

After months of lonely riding
Through the washed out desolate miles,
He met an old grey bearded man
Who spoke with a toothless smile.

"Could you tell me lad, about the war,
Is it over and done with yet?
I haven't seen a man for many a year,
But to me, that ain't no fret."

"I've seen the bright lights shining
In the cities' faraway crush,
I've left the push of the tramlines,
Where the people curse and rush."

"And I haven't seen a camel train
In Camooweal for many decades,
Or bullock teams in faraway Bourke
Since they named the Black Ace spades."

The boundary rider then replied,
"Old man, the war has been,
Camel trains have been pushed aside,
Just the same as Wagons and Teams."

But the War is over and gone long since
And the Aussies are back from their chores."
The old man replied, "I'm pleased they've retired,
Queen Victoria sure hated those Boers!!"

The Chinaman's Snake

In the hut, beside a huge vegie garden, lived a young Chinese couple. In the back of the hut was an old stove, still in use, in which wood was used for fuel. At this particular time the stove was quite cold as there wasn't any fire alight.

Jimmy the Chinaman spotted a brown snake rearing up from behind the stove. He gave a shriek, told his wife to watch the snake, while he raced up to the local pub to get help.

He finally got the message across that there was a snake in the hut. Amidst the yells, some wit mentioned something about a snake calling in for a Chinese meal. As Bluey lived between the Pub and Jimmy's place he volunteered to "Soon fix that snake, Jimmy my boy!" Bluey called at his own house, picked up his double barrelled shotgun and shortly afterwards entered the hut.

Bluey had a look about; the Chinese lady kept pointing to the back of the stove, so finally Bluey understood where the snake was last seen.

"We'll light a fire in the stove," quoted Bluey, "That'll fetch the villain out."

Next came a screech from Jimmy, who was standing about 20 yards away from the front of the hut. "Light a fire, Mrs."

So Jimmy's wife lit a fire. Meanwhile, Bluey, who had consumed a few too many beers, was standing near the stove, with the shotgun hanging slackly in his arm, peering over the top of the stove.

The stove warmed up; the snake came out fast. Jimmy's wife screeched and pointed. Both barrels exploded and blew the old stove to pieces. A great cloud of ash and dust filled half the room. The snake slithered out the front door, around the side of the hut and disappeared into long grass.

Bluey and Jimmy then went back to the local for a 'nerve steadier', while Jimmy's wife was once again left to guard the camp.

Along the Murray Flats

From the northern runs the cattle have been
    mustered,
It's years since there has been a rain or flood,
For the Cooper and the Thomson are not running
And drought has turned the river beds to mud.

Down the big stock routes of Canning and the
    Birdsville,
Where many a thousand head are straggling down;
They've crossed the white railed bridges of the
    Darling,
Soon they'll reach the flats by Wodonga town.

And the drovers, weary of the life and troubles,
Pray lots of raindrops will be falling soon;
The spoonbills and the black swans have
    migrated,
To a home along the Murray's big lagoons.

The old bull oaks are drooping in the heat waves,
While the flowering box have lost their honey
    bees,
And the whirly winds are curling ever upwards,
As screeching birds call 'protest' from their trees.

Now the cattle from the northland have been
    settled
To mix in with the southern stores and fats;
They have crossed the route between the two big
    rivers
And they're grazing on the lush green Murray
    Flats.

But the droving teams have now almost vanished,
For changes of the times must surely stay,
And diesel fumes are spread along the stock routes
As the dusty road trains rattle on their way.

We we'll keep the quart pot on the camp fire
    boiling,
And hear the night winds whisper in the pines;
The hobbles and the horse bells will be jingling,
As our memories take us back to other times.

The Coolamon Tally —1923

The drought was down on the Central West
And wheat crops ragged and light;
Teamsters were all at a standstill;
A world that looked far from bright.

A move was made to the further out,
Through tracks of dust, scrub and pine;
They drove to where the wheat was fair,
Or searched for what work they might find.

To Coolamon town a big team tramped
And camped by the Government tank,
Water was scarce, there was none for miles,
Not even the putrid and rank.

But the tank was full and also fenced
And guarded the whole night; hence,
Water was bought for a shilling a team,
Then pumped into troughs through the fence.

As the red sun set and darkness fell,
Teams were coming in by the score,
The pump broke down, and it was mid-morn'
Before the water was flowing once more.

There was little to do, but wait around;
With no money for beers or a game.
Draught horses tallied three hundred odd head,
The count on work bullocks the same.

> —Counted by J. L. Hulm
> who was on the waiting list to water his team.

46

No Man Knows

No man knows if a horse can win,
They think they do; they don't know when,
The horse doesn't know, but stop and think,
You don't see a horse putting money on men.

Man is so much smarter than horse,
Could be right or wrong, of course,
Horse runs a great race, no money for that;
Man backs it next start, horse has gone flat.

The trainer doesn't know, nor you and I,
We sometimes feel sure that we might;
But let's face it, there'd be no more races,
No jockeys, no bookies, no stipes.

We all know Good Friday fell on a Saturday,
In a hurdle race, no doubt;
We know bay horses eat more than greys,
Being many more bays about.

And we know the bookies will stand again,
The owners will come and go;
And the punter will pour his wages on
To something that no man knows.

Feathers and Fur

"It's not a j-joke," said the stuttering bloke,
"When a man g-gets soaked to the hide,
I've got spare s-socks by my t-tucker box
B-but I haven't g-got a change of strides."

"Now, don't worry Fred," his tall mate said,
"There's a spare pair of mine by the door."
But the very next day, he heard Fred say,
"They're ch-chafing my armpits r-raw."

It was trapping time, so Fred set a line,
'M-might catch a f-few bunnies perhaps."
But an eagle bold then entered the fold
And stole those rabbits from the traps.

A cry was heard, Fred trapped the bird,
Clipped it's wings, the traps he reset,
"W-walk as I do f-friend, see how you fend,
S-see how many you g-get!"

A mirror frail was hanging from a nail,
Outside of the hut, in the light,
His mate sneaked a glance, then asked by chance,
"Are you shaving outside tonight?"

With a spritely bound Fred jumped around,
Said, "Are you l-l-losing your mind,
W-what side where, d-do you grow hair,
Do you th-think I'm f-fur lined?"

Fred decided to go to the races,
And the Cup was just about on,
He then rushed up to a bookie,
"F-five shillings I'll h-have on Our Bon."

A roar from the Bookie, "Can't set you."
The lowest he'd take was ten bob —
'T-take what you c-can," cried Freddie,
"I'll g-get the rest on with the m-mob."

49

Monday Morning Blues

There's a chap from Walla Walla
Who forgot to buy his smokes;
But strolled into the lunch room
Beaming with smiles and jokes.

In the lunch room at the workshop
Stands a broken smokes machine;
A big sign 'Out of Order'
Plainly written and easily seen.

Over goes our 'Walla',
Takes the sign away,
Puts a heap of money in,
Wonders why it doesn't play.

So he kicks it, shakes it, pokes it,
But of course no smokes come out,
Then tries to get his money back,
Growls, then starts to shout.

"Hey, this crazy thing don't work,
Two bucks, and it won't repay."
Then he hangs the sign back up,
Laughs loud and walks away.

Come On Dad

The Mountain Ash were tumbling
And the axemen were a grumbling,
For the orders from the mills were over clogged;
Old Mac and Vern were racing,
While Mac's son Blue was pacing,
And jotting down the measurements of the logged.

With axes sharp as razors,
It really would amaze you,
To see the big chips flying clean away.
With their rippling muscles working,
And no time for such as shirking,
A record fall was made by Mac that day.

The camp place of their sleeping,
Was then left for the keeping
Of the scrublands, to the blustery winds and sun,
For the annual local show
Was all set and ripe to go,
There was money in the woodchops to be won.

As the starter pulled the trigger,
We were watching Old Mac's figure,
As he drove his axe then whipped it back each
      stroke,
In the lead at the halfway stop,
Mac paused, then spun on the block,
The rest of the field had given up their hope.

A voice in the crowd
Was roaring out loud,
"Go Mac, go like mad."
Then Old Mac stopped,
For his axe had dropped,
As the voice roared, "Come on Dad!"

Down To Earth

Douglas, a young chap in his mid thirties enjoyed the odd ale. As times moved on, the breathalyser began operations in our home town, Lavington. This, of course, put quite a scare into a large number of the locals; as it did in many other towns.

Douglas, like the rest of us, worked on his own ideas how to beat this latest invention.

As he lived approximately three kilometres from the 'local' he decided — too far to walk; too costly to hire a taxi, and he did like a yarn with the boys. So Douglas bought a shining two wheel push bike.

To give you an idea on Douglas' build, he was about 5'6" in height and weighed roughly fifteen stone.

The very same afternoon that he purchased his bike, he set off, whistling away, down to the Boomerang, where he joined the boys for a yarn and a few ales.

A couple of hours soon ticked away. Douglas decided to peddle off home. He bought six bottles of Carlton Draught; these were handed to him in a half size beer box. Although the bottles are loose, they fit quite neatly into this box.

Douglas strapped the box onto the carryall above the back mudguard, mounted his machine, crossed the road and then took off for home, riding along the edge of the bitumen. He had ridden about one kilometre up the road when he started to run out of puff. At the same time he heard a commotion behind him and looked around to find a semi trailer appearing to be cutting him very short on roadway.

Douglas steered sharply towards the gutter, hit a pot-hole and of course lost control. After all the wobbling and crashing came to an end, the bottles had skidded onto the highway and Douglas was on the footpath with the bike perched on top of him. He jumped up, elbows and knees skinned and bleeding, the semi was disappearing around a corner, some cars were running over a few bottles, while others were swerving to dodge the remainder.

When the traffic eased down Douglas sauntered over the roadway and gathered his six bottles. Quite amazingly none of these were broken.

KNICKELS 86

Bullocks From The Booby

Wild cattle from The Booby
On the Koscuisko side,
They crash the snow gum branches,
As wing men are racing wide.

How those bullocks rush the fences
If they're pressured from the rear,
The steam will rise from racing,
As they tremble, snort in fear.

Wild cattle from The Booby,
The mob goes racing by,
They've passed a thousand snow gums
'Neath the dark grey snowy sky.

How they wheeled, then rushed that gully
As a wild duck took to flight;
And those horsemen rode like fury
To keep the herd in sight.

Wild cattle from The Booby
They've crossed the Doubtful's bed;
Wild dogs startled from their lair,
Took to their heels and fled.

White foam from sweating horses,
Scattered high in the evening breeze;
There's cold clear water flowing
And there's grass up to their knees.

Wild cattle from The Booby
Their horns will clash and rub,
As they're racing down the Yellow Boy,*
Through the eucalyptus scrub.

To the saleyards on the Murray,
Where they're counted, split and sold,
And from every mile of mountain
There's a story to unfold.

*The Yellow Boy Trail was the main stock route from the
Upper Murray to the Grazing Leases on the western slopes of
the Snowy Mountains.

Old Habits Die Hard

Camped out by the Four Mile crossing,
Things not going too well,
Were two young lads with some cattle
And the old man giving them hell.

They eyed him off, like two strange dogs,
One frightened, the other not game,
Not a word spoke by those young blokes
And they kept on speaking the same.

"Put some wood on that fire, boys,
And toss a bit of tea in the pot,
You've been droving a few small years
And you think you know the lot."

The old man was a little touchy
And thought the young 'uns depraved,
He couldn't catch on to life's changes,
Of inflation and modern ways.

"Get a bit of bread from the township,
While you're gone I'll cook a stew,
Get a few sausages from the butcher,
A kilometre of them will do.

"In my day, boys, we'd work till dark,
Milk cows and then feed the pigs,
And just to survive we'd start at five,
Or the boss would give us the skids.

"Get a racehorse, you'll lose your buddies,
Go broke and your mates don't care;
If you can't tell lies, try horse dealing;
Milk cows, you'll soon learn to swear!"

A big red cow gave a bellow,
Back through the mob, rushed past,
The old man shouts, "You bat-eyed louts,
You've missed another calf!!

"No roaring down the tarmac
On rubber cushioned springs,
I don't know what you growl about,
You must have been born to whinge!!

"Now back in the day of the big mobs,
Fifty hours a week for the team,
We shore with the blades to perfection,
Then some fool invented a machine!

"There'd have been no hope for non working
      blokes,
You'd have never of earned your keep!!"
But the boys hadn't heard, his scornful words,
For hours they'd been asleep.

The Galloping Butterfly

There's a show of a smile as we think of those
    days;
There's no fun like the fun of the young;
We'd laugh for days in our carefree ways,
Of the small things that made so much fun.

While travelling the bush year after year,
An uncommon sight at times you'll strike,
The first occasion is the one that is clear;
Firm in the mind are those school age hikes.

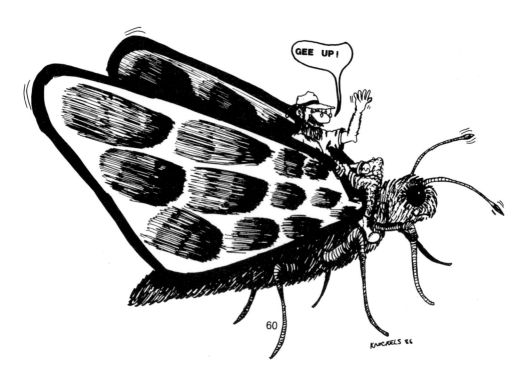

We were riding through an open bush flat,
In snow grass country miles from a camp;
We saw a chap running, waving his hat,
He'd stop and start, like a sprinting champ.

We thought, "the man's mad," so kept well clear,
He dived about with a leap and a bound,
As we gaped in amazement at a sight so queer;
He gave a hawklike dive, then hit the ground.

Up he jumped, with his hands held high;
There were patches on his backside and knees,
Corks hung from his hat, to ward off the flies,
And he sported a beard that waved in the breeze.

He spotted us then, but didn't notice our gaping,
In his hand was a butterfly, yellow and black,
He roared in excitement, the fellow was shaking,
"I'll mount this cove back at my shack!"

We wished him good day, went on down the track,
Then giggled and yabbered for miles down our
        course;
Couldn't picture a man on a butterfly's back,
As we only knew about mounting a horse.

Cracked And Blackened Feet

I am sitting by my window
With a pot of black tea, sweet;
While daylight creeps so slowly
To the rooftops in the street.

And the colours after daybreak
Have turned a faded blue,
The twinkling stars have vanished
As the sun comes peering through.

Now the roadway's getting rowdy
As the drivers race their cars,
When they're rushing to the office,
To the factory or the bars.

The children saunter by to school,
They're as neat as a navy fleet;
And the youngsters now are missing
With their cracked and blackened feet.

In my mind are bellowing cattle,
The packhorse and the rattle
Of the stirrup irons and bells and hobble chains.
But I hear the mothers calling,
While a shower of rain is falling,
As it washes rubbish down the concrete drains.

Did I hear a scrub bull bellow
As he called a challenge to fight?
Or did I hear the air brakes
Of a semi through the night?

Trucks roar by on the highway
In a racing, endless run;
They're trading freight in cities,
For the contracts have been won.

We care of the past, and old timers,
How they battled to make their way,
And broke that back of harshness,
To build the life style of today.

We now thank those past generations;
And pray that we never will meet,
Those children on their way to school
With their cracked and blackened feet.

Gone Fishing

The cart horse days were dying
When tracks were still main roads,
Vehicles were becoming popular,
As they helped to lighten loads.

The boys had an old T model ute;
Daybreak they'd be up and about,
Travel for miles to a decent stream,
As they loved to chase after trout.

They rolled the ute, all wheels up,
As she missed some rough U-turns;
Their bait tin smashed, it had carried
Sawdust, woodgrubs and worms.

Those young men scrambled out,
Quite dazed and a little upset;
Tom could not understand why
His head felt clammy and wet.

Their tucker box was broken,
The grease tin mixed with bread,
Sawdust and broken woodgrubs
Covered his back and head.

"Are you all right mate?" asked Joe.
Tom said, "I'm feeling quite strong,
But give me a hand for a moment,
Pop my brains back where they belong!!"

Clearing Sale

Went to a sale a few years back,
Goods of all types, piled in rough stacks,
A clearing sale; the land had been sold,
Some goods new, others rusty and old.

The auctioneer roared, "How much the camp
     oven?"
The crowd weren't bidding, just kept on shovin'
While the urgers were busy with note book and
     pens,
"What am I bid, on the rooster and hens?"

A rusty set of hobbles, discarded years ago,
With a blackened old quart pot on show,
A one dollar bid, knocked down to me;
It matters but little; memories are free.

A five year old bay, proud carriage, good head,
'He's a real nasty type," the dealer had said,
"Don't touch that horse, his stifle is bad."
He threw in a bid; I knew I'd been had.

A kelpie pup, on a chain of wire,
Had a good broad head; full of fire,
"Done, all done," an urger spoke.
"Left in the hands of the camp oven bloke."

The sale all over, the crowd all away,
Prices of goods was the talk that day,
"Much too dear," was the cockie's wail.
But they'll bid again, at the next clearing sale.

Snow Grass Races (Yarrangobilly*)

The village population,
Having considered racin'
Got together, six or so of them;
Then tore from a paddock
The scrub with a mattock,
Tossed aside the rocks, those keen men.

Five furlongs were found,
Up, down and around,
And never a sign of a flat.
In the snow grass thick
There were holes and sticks;
Of course, no one cared about that.

The bookies and the beer
Were plentiful and clear,
Things that a race man sought most;
The tucker was neat
And the crowd had a treat,
Near the Snow Grass winning post.

Pack horse races,
Greasy pig chases,
All types of events added fun;
Where the cold river churns
By the two furlong turns,
A trout catching comp' was being run.

A few hundred people
Had a great day's fun,
Then they danced all night
'Til the rise of the sun.

No sleep to be had,
For then we'd pack up;
Tighten the girth straps
And head off for the hut.

*Between Tumut and Kiandra.

69

KNICKELS 86

Near Enough

Old Patch, a mate of mine
Worked hard on a line
Of fence, for a cocky, 'Careful' Blight.
Camped beneath a tree,
The shade rent free,
But the dirt and rocks were tight.

As he toiled away
For many a day,
'Careful' followed him along
And gave a post a crack,
Then jerked the wire back,
Checking if the fence was strong.

When 'Careful' asked Patch,
If the fence was up to scratch,
Patch replied, "Near enough, Mr Blight".
'Careful's' voice was gruff,
"Near enough's not good enough,
The damn thing's gotta be right".

'Careful' stood up higher,
Peered along the wire,
Patch thought, 'The lousy old tough',
But asked, "Mr Blight,
Do you think its right?"
'Careful' said, "Near enough, near enough!!"

KNICKELS 86

Riders of *Jagumba Hills

The loose slush flew as the racing crew
Rushed their steeds to head off the lead,
While the wing men swore as the brumbies tore,
And then broke with a lightning speed.

'Rum' was trapped; around a wattle wrapped,
And his horse bolted off in a flash;
He was later found, sitting up on the ground,
Without memory of the chase or the crash.

With the brumbies tough and the 'going' rough,
The horsemen were all racing hard,
There was still a show that the mob would go
To the rails of the big Ash yard.

With the pace so quick and the saplings thick
Old Blue somehow lost his course;
A wit roared, "Too slow, he's let a tree grow,
Between his backside and his horse!!"

*On western slopes of Snowy Mountains of N.S.W.

We Can't Have An Aussie Beer

We can eat a leaf of cabbage
No calories in that, My Dear;
We can have an egg without any salt,
But we can't have an Aussie Beer.

A slice of toast so hard and dry,
Not a sign of a good rump steak;
We pick away at a lettuce leaf,
But the system's hard to break.

For in these days of the diet craze
We can't eat this or that,
We can't eat sugar, we can't eat salt
And we're barred from meat with fat.

We tip toe up to the old fridge door
Where the contents look so queer;
Tins all branded with a diet stamp,
But no sign of an Aussie Beer.

For in the place of a juicy steak
Is a smiling half grapefruit,
It looks about as appealing
As a farmer's worn out boot.

We'll keep control for a month or two,
Lose a little weight, no fears,
No household chores, the wireless roars,
And we've lost our Aussie beers.

Now the wife never reads this rubbish.
The daughters say the old man's queer,
When they rave about some TV show,
How I long for a beaut Aussie beer.

The Little Aussie Battlers

Pure breeds, cross breeds and others,
Backbone of the travelling mobs,
We'd be at a loss without them,
Those flea bitten, scrawny dogs.

Some dogs are like a crocodile,
Seem to only close one eye
At night, and never lose a sheep,
While ever there's life in their hide.

Other dogs curl up in a ball,
Fall asleep with the coming of dark;
The sheep could use them for hurdles,
Those hounds wouldn't utter a bark.

Some wake cranky at daylight,
Snarling and rearing to fight,
Then snap all day at the workers,
At the toiler that watched all night.

They strut around with an 'I'm boss' look,
With a flash stiff legged tramp,
When the going gets a little tough,
Sneak off and look for a camp.

Others hungry and sore footed,
Tired from continual slave,
Will stick to their work forever,
Till the day they reach their grave.

One dog raced in small circles,
As around the mob he flew,
Had been tied up for a couple of years,
'Twas the only thing he knew.

Another old dog, a high stepper,
Front paws reached out, full of grace,
This old chap only owned one gear,
A very slow trot was top pace.

Some tread careful in thistles,
Howl, hold a foot up high;
Others race through like demons
And never bat an eye.

Work to some comes natural,
Others that would never learn,
But a real bad dog will sometimes
Do you a real top turn.

Our sheep dog breed is solid,
All colours, black and red,
If those battlers form a union,
There'll be big, big trouble ahead.

*P.S. "Cumberoona"

"We'll scrub and polish the deck throughout,
Put a shine on the kitchen gear;
We'll watch the towering red gums wave
And the black man with his spear.

"Oh, we'll steal a keg of the Captain's rum
And steam down the river once more,
We'll fish and swim, have lots of fun
As we did in the days of yore."

Deep thoughts were put into action
In the year of Eighty five,
To build another big steamboat
And to keep the past alive.

Old Cumberoona won the vote
As the blueprint for the plan,
A committee quickly gathered around
And the hard work then began.

The premier came to launch her;
She went sliding down the slope,
Then gave a lurch and shuddered,
But was held by a safety rope.

She dipped her bow into the stream
As a pelican dips her beak,
Gave a plunge, then straightened up;
Proud, without sign of a leak.

The Cumberoona's whistle blew,
She turned to the river's flow,
As the Captain bellowed orders,
"Full steam ahead, down below!!"

She swept around a willowy bend
As the paddles paved the way,
The stoker hot in the engine room,
Cursed his luck and his pay.

The Cumberoona lives once more,
To return to her daily run;
We'll steer her down the Murray's course
To battle with the wind and sun.

We'll venture far up the 'Bidgee,
Stop at every port of call;
Then move along the Lachlan
And trade our goods with all.

The barefoot children shout and play
As we leave the river's shore;
The Captain gives the horn a blast
And we're on our way once more.

We meet with the Lachlan steamers,
Their tug-boats topped up full;
The long ropes have been knotted
Over bales of western wool.

Our freight is dropped at Adelaide
To be shipped far across the sea;
We then load up and return again
On the waterways of the free.

A big horse team goes plodding by
In the dust with a farmer's plough;
A lad with a pup and a bucket,
Saunters off to milk his cow.

"We'll scrub and polish the deck throughout,
Put a shine on the kitchen gear;
We'll watch the towering red gums wave,
And the black man with his spear.

"Oh, we'll steal a keg of the Captain's rum
And steam down the river once more,
We'll fish and swim, have lots of fun,
As we did in the days of yore."

*Paddle steamer, "Cumberoona" built by a local committee
on the Murray River at Albury, 1986

78

The Painted Snake

Bill and Mary had been married for about 12 months. As usual, for a Saturday afternoon, Bill went up to the 'local' for a few ales and a yarn to the boys.

After a few hours a 'phone call came through for Bill. Mary was on the other end. "Bill", said Mary, "There is a big brown snake on the verandah!"

From Bill, "Don't be telling me about it, get the shotgun and shoot it."

Mary said, "No, I haven't shot a snake before."

Bill interrupted with, "Shoot it." Then put the 'phone down and turned around to the boys, "Woman's got to learn to kill a snake, a man could be a hundred miles away."

On the verandah was one snake, also five new one gallon tins of paint of different colours. The paint had been bought by Bill in the morning and lined hurriedly up against the wall.

Bill arrived home much later, also very chirpy. By this time the house lights were out and Mary was in bed. Bill called out, "How'd you get along with old 'Joe Blake' love?" Quietly from Mary, "Missed it". "Ha, Ha," laughed Bill, "How could anyone miss an old snake with a shotgun?" No answer.

Next morning, Bill a little seedy, sauntered out to shift his tins of paint to the back shed.

There were five paint tins blown to pieces, paint splattered over the verandah and high up the wall; and of course, no snake.

The Luckless Few

Hello there, how's the problems
In your treeless, smog filled town,
Do you ever try at smiling?
It will beat that sullen frown.

You'll never know your neighbour
And you barely know your folk,
You don't have time to have a yarn
And you never seem to joke.

But you'll laugh about that neighbour
As he staggers home so late,
When his highly valued guard dog
Won't allow him in the gate.

You'll rush home from the factory
With night plans laid out neat;
While youngsters in their boredom
Form their gangs along the street.

As you settle down in comfort
To eat bush grown supplies,
Please spare a thought for cockies
And the heat and dust and flies.

How you charge off in the morning
To that never ending jam,
As you rush and push and bustle
To catch a bus or tram.

You wonder why the country folk,
When they growl at milking cows,
Do not short cut bad seasons
Like you did your forty hours.

But the bird's a different colour
When that yearly trip comes around,
As your 'phone keeps on a ringing
And you just cannot be found.

Ah, you've motored to the wonderland
Where you camp and fish and dream,
And drive about the mountains
With her cool clear lakes and streams.

I don't care much for smokes and drinks
But there's two things I really hate;
One is when I'm out of smokes,
And when the 'booze bus' is late.

It's all a joke, don't get me wrong,
I'm sure we'll get along fine,
As I've been doing the same as you,
For quite a long, long time.

The Mighty *Mitta Muster

The country folk are gathered strong
Where the Mitta runs her course;
Crowds roar loud to voice their cheers,
To a winner and his horse.

A great day's fun to be had by all;
The committee's efforts are grand,
Many months work to make this show
The best muster in the land.

Youngsters brush their favourite 'nags',
Smartly walk them forth and back;
Oldies puff their pipes and chat,
"Not a real bad show, eh Jack!"

We see the weeping willows wave
Where the river gurgles through;
Horsemen race and lose their hats;
With the mountains clear in view.

Horse floats rattle by Snowy Creek,
From over the Gippsland side;
A stern judge watches man and beast,
As the crowd roars, "Ride, man ride!!"

There was talk of big North Eastern floods,
Bush fires in the far off hills;
Cattlemen spoke of the high plains grass;
While sharing the muster's thrills.

How they scoot around the flag sticks,
To a roar of, "Go, boy, go!!"
And the tops of gums sway gently,
As cool valley breezes blow.

And down from the Old Monaro
Came bush horsemen with their fray,
They laughed and boozed, spun their jokes
Of mountain men and their way.

As axemen toil, their muscles strain
And the chips fly high and wide;
Young lads throw at knock-em-downs,
Tug-o-war men puff and slide.

Ladies so busy around the tents,
Cooking and selling their wares;
The onlookers are smiling and happy,
Far away from their worries and cares.

In a land of native wild life;
The black ducks cry in flight;
Possums peer from tall gum trees
As wild dogs howl at night.

Hands of time have turned once more,
But again we'll surely cluster;
There is no doubt that we'll be back
For next year's Mighty Muster.

*In North East Victoria, Mitta Mitta

The '38 Shift

Mangoplah to Tumbarumba
1938

When we left Mango'
To go to the hills,
We sold all the good gear
To pay all the bills;
Then up to Kalua.
Full of rabbits and 'roos,
John's Wort and briars,
And three miles to school.

Floods tore down fences,
The roof leaked like hell,
Oat crops looked short,
The 'roos looked real well;
Horses would throw us,
Chase us out of the yard,
Milkers would kick us,
The wood was rock hard.

Frosts a bit solid,
Wouldn't break with a pick,
Be late for school,
Then cop a fair six.
A thousand odd acres,
It must have been fair,
For every known varmit
Seemed to live there.

Odd times the oldies would
Duck in for a beer,
But the youngsters too busy
Draughting out steers,
Milk cows, chop the wood,
Feed the horses and hens,
But given the chance,
We'd do it again.

Festival Of Nariel Creek

The weeping willows wave and float
Where the branches meet the streams;
The Rainbow trout will rise then dart
Away from the sunlight beams.

But this is a tale of a different shade,
—And I'm led to believe it's true —
Of a festival held near a mountain creek,
Where folk danced the whole night through.

'Twas all low gear for the first few hours,
—But the crowd was agathering fast —
They hit top gear as the bands warmed up
And joined in the revelry's blast.

'There'll be Tooheys and Fosters
The Slims and the Costers
At the Nariel Creek Festival this year,
There'll be singing and clapping,
And the kegs we'll be tapping,
We'll be downing our lovely cold beer!

Those empty stubbies littered the ground
While the barbecues sizzled and spat,
The young ones jumped, yelled and sang
While the oldies sipped and just sat.

The sun shone down with a burning heat,
A guy half sprung shook his head,
"We'll do a strip, have a lovely cool swim."
And his 'old chap' was burnt ruby red!!

Home, next day to mum and the kids,
And his story seemed somewhat thin,
His wife cried aloud, "Lord, look at that,
Like a rattlesnake shedding its skin!!"

'There'll be Tooheys and Fosters,
The Slims and the Costers,
At the Nariel Creek Festival this year.
There'll be singing and clapping,
And the kegs we'll be tapping,
We'll be downing our lovely cold beer.'

KNICKELS 86

A Barefooted Lie

Some stories are weak and others so strong;
Many seem to grow as the years roll on,
For it seems old Smut was a real Rugby tough,
And he claims a record - kicking goals in the
     rough.

"I used to kick goals, beyond the halfway line,
We used jam tins then, way back in my time,
Now drink up lads." — Here a slight delay
"Course I played barefooted, back in my day!!"

Foxy?

Donnie told his yarn at The Holbrook Hotel, after travelling through the bush from Tumbarumba.

As fox skins were worth about $40 each that winter, Donnie would at most times have his shotgun in his car, for, "You never know from where a fox will spring."

He stopped his car beside a rough, bracken covered gully, got his fox whistle and shotgun from the car and selected a position where he stood very still, and blew the whistle. He then realized that he had only one cartridge in the gun and did not have any more in the car. Of course, if a fox did trot up, that shouldn't cause any problem.

However, a few minutes later along came two foxes, but about ten yards apart. Donnie waited patiently, hoping that the foxes would brush close together, so that he would have a chance of shooting both. A few seconds ticked by and the foxes were getting very close to Donnie, but still a long way apart. According to Donnie there was only one thing left to do; "I gave them the old 'swoosh shot' and I got them both!!"

The Old And The New

Camel trains long, bullock teams strong,
Shoved aside for the big steam trains;
Horse teams too, as the rubber wheels grew,
Now only their ghost remains.

The hand made leather harness,
Was hung in the sheds, then forgotten;
Wagons and drays were given away,
Or out in the weather, went rotten.

The swaggie would call at the homestead,
Try out his luck for a feed,
He'd chop the wood or cut our burrs,
For that was his way and creed.

For many a mile he humped that swag
And a billy can all askew,
But fell in a heap, like the chimney sweep,
As things progressed and grew.

The river boats were left afloat,
Chained tight near a river bank,
They couldn't compete, with the petrol fleet;
And remained till they rotted and sank.

Shearing blades had lost their grade,
Machines made them look like fools;
The backyard dike was given the hike,
Then used to house garden tools.

Bag rugs left horses,
Tarps next - water proof;
Coloured tiles on houses,
Outshone the old tin roof.

Feather beds flew the coop
When kapok hit the sack;
Carpet rolled in every room,
Lino shot out the back.

Travelling homes or caravans
Caused the tents to collapse;
Corks popped out of bottles,
On came plastic caps.

Water coolers washed away,
Fridges froze them slack;
Electric stoves proved too hot,
Burnt the wood types black.

Fine telescopic sights,
Outraced kangaroo dogs;
Thin pieces of cotton lace
Out stripped swimming togs.

Tough, cold crumbling damper,
Cut out by fresh sliced bread;
Porridge from rough ground wheat;
Was left by Weeties for dead.

Digging out those rabbits
Eased off with supplies of traps,
Then mixo' came with a flourish,
Wiped ferrets off the maps.

The kero lamp was given the tramp
As power lines started to roam;
When T.V.'s entered doorways
Conversation left the home.

That kelly axe has lost much use
As power saws roared and ripped;
Butter churns have long been spurned,
On the rubbish heap, been tipped.

Sulkies and carts tipped over a bank
As the motors took their place;
'Dozer blades outshovelled spades,
Put a smile on many a face.

Electric blankets warmed things up,
House cats got the chop;
Wide combs turned snaggers to shearers,
Roustabouts ran red hot.

Now this is the cry, we must live high,
But we're pushing our luck up hill;
Rent hard to pay and been that way
Since we shrunk the Dollar Bill.

KNICKELS 86

Opening Day On The Weir

The day's work over, trailers are stacked,
Blankets, tucker and guns well packed;
A charge from town as the sun sinks low,
Then the tents are pitched and the fires glow.

It's opening day and there's lots of cheer,
Thousands of shooters and boat loads of beer;
It's break of day, we're trying our luck,
There's fun and games, but not for the duck.

The noise would deafen an army drill,
As the echoes dance and can't stay still;
The birds circle high in a puzzled fear
Of continuous roar on the old Hume Weir.*

We tossed a rubber duck into a lagoon,
It's seen by a flock, they'll be coming in soon;
We sit very still as the birds turn back,
Then lured them in with our best 'Quack Quack'.

A few fly low; boom, boom once more,
The big flock veers away from the shore,
To search for quieter waters far away,
For it's not to be found about here today.

By the edge of the lake a water hen sneaks,
Where the willow limbs and the water meets;
An old galah gives an angry screech;
Cormorants go wild in their hasty retreat.

We bagged a few ducks, the day has been fine,
Our stubbies way under the Plimsol Line,
The gear all packed and we're on our way,
Back to the pub to top up our day.

*Albury, N.S.W.

Not To Be Had

Tom the butcher was a friendly guy
And looked after his customers strong,
They paid their bills like honest folk
And very few treated him wrong.

Of course there's sometimes an odd one
Keen to hand out a bum steer,
Pitch a good yarn and book up meat,
Then go and pay cash for their beer.

But Sortie booked up far too long
And created an awkward position;
So butcher Tom was cut down cold;
Sortie bought from the opposition.

Tom was having a chat to friends
While strolling along the street;
Lo and behold, he met Sortie,
Carrying a big bag of meat.

"You're surely tough," Tom spoke firm,
"Are you playing some kind of joke,
You get your hands on a little cash,
Then you buy from the other bloke!"

"Settle down old man," said Sortie,
"And keep yourself out of a spin,
Don't kid yourself right up the wall,
For I'm doing the same to him!!"

Yap-Yap

During 1955, when the Snowy Mountains Scheme was in full swing, Eddie, a chap who had been working there for quite a few years teamed up with two immigrants from Hungary, named Frank and Steve. Steve had been caring for a mongrel fox terrier type dog that was running around the camp at Guthega, where they were stationed. One Sunday they decided to go down along the Snowy River to do a bit of fishing, and of course, Steve had to take the dog.

They pulled up at a small clearing by the river, which was to be their base for the day. Eddie and Frank went their various ways along the river, while Steve stayed on and got a fire going and prepared a snack.

The dog took off into the bush, hunting for anything that moved. In a short time Steve could hear the dog, "Yap-yap, yap-yap", then the dog came out of the bush, yapping away and following a strange looking reptile, that was racing straight towards the camp. Steve, not knowing anything about a goanna, or even knowing what it was, stood there with his mouth open, perhaps wondering why it was heading towards him.

The next event was to be one that Steve would never forget, for the goanna clawed its way to the top of his head in a few short seconds. The dog was yapping away madly and as blood was rolling down Steve's face and arms from the claws of the enraged goanna, Steve gave a terrified yell. Eddie heard the commotion, raced over and caught the dog, then threw it into the river.

The goanna jumped down and strutted off with head and tail high in the air.

As soon as the dog got out of the river, it yap yapped after the goanna again, but by this time the goanna had found safety in a tall tree.

Apart from being shaken up and having forty one stitches inserted where the goanna had ripped him, Steve was quite all right.

KNICKELS 86

The Hair Of The Dog, No Thanks

The woolies strung over the Harbour Bridge,
Another mob Pitt Street way,
For shearing was on at the Opera House
And the clerks shore fifteen a day.

The brass band played for the pickers up,
The cook strutted round like a lord,
While the Mayor and his wife were the pressers,
The tar boy turned Boss of the Board.

Some down town scholar with an eye for a dollar,
Tried to kill the wild life trade,
In that lovely 'roo meat, he sneaked rough beef,
T-bone, sirloin and blade.

On the plains they were damming the creek beds,
Tore down the big wind mills,
They worked and slaved, water must be saved,
To irrigate the Snowy Mountains hills.

They were ploughing Randwick Racecourse,
To grow, then cut the chaff,
For the station hacks from outer back,
To make the slow run fast.

Politicians were driving 'dozers,
Graders and rollers grouse,
Patching up the highway;
The unemployed ran Canberra House.

Doctors were all timber felling,
For they were all short of brass,
The kangaroos carried shot guns;
Cockies were thieving their grass.

He woke, crook, hot and shaky,
Groaned as he turned in the cot,
"That's all through, like a backyard loo;
I'll never again touch a drop!"

Ode To The Packhorse

Farewell, farewell my bewildered friend;
How could we know that this was the end?
You wonder why you're left so neglected,
Now so old and so hurt and dejected.

You shared your grass with the kangaroos,
A wild boar pig and a few emus.
You'd watch them depart as snow fell thick,
They'd scatter like winds over gully and stick.

To vanish away through the boundary fence,
They left you lonely, worried and tense,
Then the loneliness fled and the thoughts to roam,
Were forgotten thoughts, for you were at home.

You'd dash through the scrub at a frightening rate,
And skid to a halt at the boundary gate,
Then race to the stockyard, prop and wheel,
With the ghost of a wild dog at your heel.

The merino sheep and the white faced steers
Would race and split in their sudden fears,
As you raced so close in your frolicking fun,
Then you quietly turned, just to watch them run.

And the slightest sound you could hear so well,
A light crack of a whip or a faraway bell;
Then you'd turn and graze in the early dew;
We'd hazard a guess, how you always knew.

Now your young pals race, perhaps think you're
    slack,
As you slowly plod, along the river flat,
But your friends don't know of the mountain
    tracks
And the many long years that you carried the
    packs.

Oh, it's all gone now and the hills are dead,
On steep stock trails you'll never more tread,
It's tough, Old Mate, but we can't change ways;
For the gates are closed on your droving days.

Travelling Man

As youngsters, we lived for many years along the Mannus Creek, on our property *"Kalua". There were a number of sad occasions during these years, but luckily the fun and thrills outnumbered these.

During the 1940's the Forestry Commission built some huts for their workmen. These were situated about half a mile upstream from our home and roughly a hundred yards from the bank of the creek.

To get across the creek the men used a raft which consisted of three x 44 gallon drums wired together. This was attached by a wire to a cable which was firmly secured to a solid post on either side of the creek.

On one occasion the creek was flooded, and too dangerous to enter, even on a strong swimming horse.

One of the workmen, Les Henderson had to raft across to handle a chore of some kind on the

opposite side. About half way across, the wire holding the raft to the cable broke and away went Les on the raft.

There were a couple of blokes running along the edge of the creek,yelling instructions to Les, while another ran back to the camp for a rope; but it was only a few minutes before Les disappeared around a bend in the creek and on his way into big trouble.

A few hundred yards further downstream was a tunnel, where the water turned really rough, creating whirl pools and charging amongst rocks into much lower country.

Another chap, walking along the creek, spotted this strange outfit, and as Les got a little closer, despite his fears, he didn't lose his sense of humour, for he called out as he went by, "Is this the way to Mildura?"

However, the current tossed Les and the raft out of the main stream into shallow water and Les got out soaking wet, but laughing away in his usual manner.

*Kalua, in Tumbarumba Shire, N.S.W.

The Craft Of The Crow

The Jackass laughed at the black Crow's craft,
Crow was perched on a dry limb, high
Amongst old dead trees, where he caught the
    breeze,
While he studied the farm, with a careful eye.

"One would never know," said the old black Crow,
"I've the patience of a governor's guard,
For maybe a mouse will run from the house,
Or a chicken will stray from its yard."

The Eagle up high, peered down from the sky,
As he watched for a rabbit or a snake,
"Perhaps I will snare, a big fat hare;
What a lovely feast he would make."

"It's not my day," said the young black Jay,
"All the worms must have gone underground,
With the weather so great, they must have slept
    late,
There's not a grub, worm or snail to be found."

The rain birds squabbled as the blue Crane
    wobbled,
With a jerky step as he peered in the creek,
He only saw the water, and thought that he
    'oughter'
Move away and chase, whatever Swallows seek.

From a young Curlew shy, came a mournful cry,
As it called its mate, that wasn't coming back;
And the little sparrow squawked and the pigeon
    baulked
As a hawk swooped down, looking for a snack.

'Twas just after dark, the Fox gave a bark,
And called the flock together for a meeting,
"At daybreak meet here, and never have a fear,
I'll introduce you to the goods of farmer Keating."

As daylight broke through, the Fox and his crew
Had a feast from the farmer's fowl pen,
With the garden picked bare, the Fox set his snare,
As he welcomed them home to his den.

But the cunning old Crow, said, "I must go,
For I'm a very busy bird these days."
With a couple of springs, and a flap of his wings,
Said goodbye to that Fox and his scheming ways

To Beat The Odds

Now I'll tell you a tale and a good one,
Of a loss turned to gain, without luck;
How a small fishing crew with some set lines,
Brought a Fishing Inspector unstuck.

Those Inspectors of Fisheries are toughies,
They are surely not types to be bought,
And this yarn didn't get to the papers,
For it didn't get into the court.

There was Donnie the runner and Arnie,
By the edge of a lake, with young Bill;
And a lawman that hovered in shadows,
For to book a wrong doer was a thrill.

But close to the camp he was sighted;
Young Bill said, "Here's trouble, I'd say".
"Never fear, we'll be right," spoke up Donnie,
"Don't run, just watch how I play."

So Donnie the runner went racing,
A fleet footed Inspector in tow,
The Lawman soon tackled our Donnie,
Who then pulled out his licence to show.

The Lawman spoke, "Son, why the hurry,
Your licence holds good, what's the rot?"
Donnie said quietly, "It's the others,
A licence, they just haven't got!!"

A Little Touch Of Bushy

The new Town Hall
Could crash and fall,
Be forgotten the very next day,
But you know that scene
Of the place you'd been,
On your bushland holiday.

So you pack some scran
Throw it in the van,
The wife and the kids are keen,
Then head that bus
On a track of dust,
To the smallest lake to be seen.

As you pitch your tent
You'll forget about rent,
The mortgage at home, or the toil,
A slight breeze blowing,
The camp fire glowing
As you're waiting for the billy to boil.

There's no flash grub
While you're in the scrub,
You'll act like the Aussie that you are,
When you gnash your teeth
On a lump of cold beef,
You'll be proud, and free as the stars.

Well, I'd better not push
Or you'll all go bush,
When the weekend or holidays fall,
Then we wouldn't find peace
That we so often seek
For there's A LITTLE TOUCH OF BUSHY in us
    all.

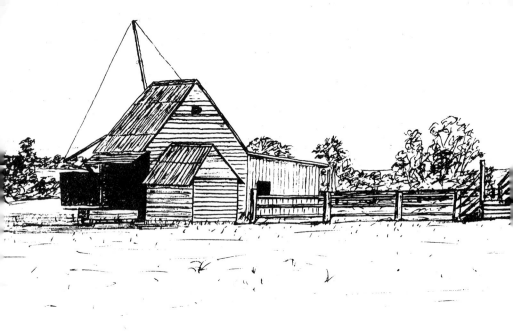

An old killing works on the outskirts of Tumbarumba, N.S.W. As there are very few of these buildings still standing, those left must certainly be top candidates for Historical Societies.

The killing of animals in this type of building ceased around 1960 and all operations were then carried out in the much larger abattoirs.

As a few of the stories in "Aussie Bush Yarns" are 'a little close to home', I thank those concerned for granting permission to print the same. I would also like to thank those who helped out regarding typing and editing.

Sincerely,
Neil Hulm.,